Contents

The Lighthouse Keeper's Secret

A slippery tale of . . .

S tory-teller

  L ighthouse Keeper

    I ris, the daughter

      M other

        E ye-patch Jake

The scene is a downstairs kitchen in the lighthouse. There is a chair and a stove with a pot on it. It is dark and a bad storm howls outside. A flashing torch on a small table will serve as the great lamp. Each time someone climbs up or down the tower, he or she should go round and round this lamp many times, with heavy strides.

A complete list of Spirals

Stories

Jim Alderson
Crash in the Jungle
The Witch Princess

Jan Carew
Death Comes to the Circus

Susan Duberley
The Ring

**Keith Fletcher and
Susan Duberley**
Nightmare Lake

John Goodwin
Dead-end Job

Paul Groves
Not that I'm Work-shy
The Third Climber

Anita Jackson
The Actor
The Austin Seven
Bennet Manor
Dreams
The Ear
A Game of Life or Death
No Rent to Pay

Paul Jennings
Eye of Evil
Maggot

Margaret Loxton
The Dark Shadow

Patrick Nobes
Ghost Writer

Kevin Philbin
Summer of the Werewolf

John Townsend
Beware of the Morris Minor
Fame and Fortune
SOS

David Walke
Dollars in the Dust

Plays

Jan Carew
Computer Killer
No Entry
Time Loop

John Godfrey
When I Count to Three

Nigel Gray
An Earwig in the Ear

Paul Groves
Tell Me Where it Hurts

Barbara Mitchelhill
Punchlines
The Ramsbottoms at Home

Madeline Sotheby
Hard Times at Batwing Hall

John Townsend
Cheer and Groan
The End of the Line
Hanging by a Fred
The Lighthouse Keeper's Secret
Making a Splash
Murder at Muckleby Manor
Over and Out
Taking the Plunge

David Walke
The Bungle Gang Strikes Again
The Good, the Bad and the Bungle
Package Holiday

The Lighthouse Keeper's Secret

Story-teller	This is a tale to chill you to the bone.
Lighthouse keeper	Brrrr . . . it's right nippy tonight.
Story-teller	There you are, I told you so. Yes, this is a tale to freeze your nerves. To turn your heart to ice. To turn your knees to jelly. To make your blood run cold . . .
Lighthouse keeper	Then I'd better put another lump of coal on the fire.
Mother	I'll heat up the supper and put the cat out.
Iris	But mother, this is a lighthouse perched up on a single rock with roaring sea on every side.
Mother	So that's why that cat always looks so rough in the mornings.
Lighthouse keeper	Ay, it's right groggy and soggy is that moggy.
Story-teller	This is a tale to send a shiver down your spine . . .

Lighthouse keeper	Brrrrrr . . .
Iris	What's up, father?
Lighthouse keeper	It's as if someone has just walked over my grave.
Mother	Don't be daft, you want to be buried at sea.
Lighthouse keeper	It was a shiver. It just shot down my spine, ran right down my trouser leg and straight into the cat's saucer of milk. Look, it's now frozen solid.
Mother	The milk?
Lighthouse keeper	No, the cat.
Iris	Oooh, mother, just hark at that wind.
Story-teller	Wooooosh . . . shshshshshs . . . swishshshshshsh . . .
Mother	Ay, it's a dark and stormy night all right tonight.
Story-teller	It was a dark and stormy night . . .
Lighthouse keeper	She's just said that bit.
Mother	Yes, I've just said that.
Story-teller	It was a very dark and stormy night. The wind howled at the one solid iron door. Wooooooooooooshshshshshsh!

Lighthouse keeper	Just hark at that wind howling at the one solid iron door.
Story-teller	The great waves lashed up at every window. Lash splash splash!
Mother	Just hark at those great waves lashing up at every window.
Story-teller	The spray froze into icicles on the lighthouse walls.
Lighthouse keeper	Just hark at the spray freezing into icicles on the lighthouse walls.
Iris	I can't hear it. Anyway, icicles don't make a noise.
Lighthouse keeper	That's a relief, I thought my hearing had gone. But look at the time, it's almost nightfall.
Story-teller	Bang . . . crash . . . wallop.
Iris	Eek, what was that?
Lighthouse keeper	Night – it just fell. So now, my dears, I must be up to work. I must climb those stairs and light the lamp. The lamp to save those poor sailors out there on this dark and stormy night. I pity any ship out there now. At least they will have our light to save them from the rocks. So up I shall go,

3

taking a candle with me. [*He begins walking round and round*] Up and up and up. Round and round and round.

Story-teller	So up he went. Up and up and up. Round and round and round. Up and round, up and round, up and round, up and round . . .
Lighthouse keeper	Round and up, round and up, round and up. Time for a swig.
Story-teller	He took a nip of rum. Then, rising in a spiral, he climbed ever higher. Stair after stair, twisting . . . turning . . . up and up and up . . .
Lighthouse keeper	Round and round and round . . .
Story-teller	Upward, climbing upward . . .
Lighthouse keeper	Up and . . .
Story-teller	Round. Round and . . .
Lighthouse keeper	Up.
Story-teller	Until at last he reached . . .
Lighthouse keeper	Half way! And another tot of rum. Up some more . . .
Story-teller	And round a bit . . .
Lighthouse keeper	And up a bit . . .
Story-teller	Up and up and up.

Lighthouse keeper	Round and round and round.
Story-teller	Upward ever upward.
Lighthouse keeper	Up and round . . .
Story-teller	Round and up.
Lighthouse keeper	Until at last . . .
Story-teller	He reached the top.
Lighthouse keeper	Phew! Another sip! At least it keeps me fit . . . [*He coughs*]
Story-teller	The great lamp stood in front of him.
Lighthouse keeper	The great lamp stands in front of me.
Story-teller	Its wick would be a beacon for all to see.
Lighthouse keeper	Its wick will be a beacon for all to see. So I turn on the oil . . .
Story-teller	He turned on the oil.
Lighthouse keeper	I put the flame to the wick.
Story-teller	He put the flame to the wick. A flicker, then a flash . . .
Lighthouse keeper	And she's alight! Well that's another day's work done! And now the beam will flash across the dark ocean.
Story-teller	The beam flashed across the dark ocean.

Lighthouse keeper	Over the angry sea.
Story-teller	Over the angry sea.
Lighthouse keeper	Through the howling storm.
Story-teller	Through the howling storm.
Lighthouse keeper	Just hark at that echo.
Story-teller	Just hark at that echo.
Lighthouse keeper	I'll just have a nip of rum . . .
Story-teller	I'll just have a . . . And the lighthouse keeper rested before the downward plod.
Lighthouse keeper	But before I go back down to my dear wife and daughter, there is one thing I must do.
Story-teller	His icy hand fumbled in his pocket.
Lighthouse keeper	The key . . . the key . . . where is the key . . .?
Story-teller	He searched . . . and searched again . . .
Lighthouse keeper	It's not here. Have you got it?
Story-teller	Of course I haven't got it. When did you have it last?
Lighthouse keeper	Well if I knew that I wouldn't have lost it, would I?

Story-teller	Well it must be somewhere.
Lighthouse keeper	Of course it's somewhere – but it's not here. Keep talking.
Story-teller	His icy hand kept on fumbling in his pocket . . . every nook, every cranny . . . and every nook again. Every little place a key might be. Have you got it yet?
Lighthouse keeper	Aha! Here it is – at last.
Story-teller	And he made his way over to the shadows where a large sea-chest stood locked and bolted.
Lighthouse keeper	Here it is! My pride and joy . . . my little secret, my . . . this lock is rusty.
Story-teller	After much twisting and turning . . .
Lighthouse keeper	Come on my little beauty.
Story-teller	And turning and twisting . . .
Lighthouse keeper	Open will you? [*He coughs and splutters*] I've always had a lot of trouble with this chest of mine.
Story-teller	Then you should give up your pipe.
Lighthouse keeper	Aha! She's open!
Story-teller	And with that, he slowly lifted the heavy, dusty lid.

Lighthouse keeper	Every night I creep up here to make sure. I make sure it's safe.
Story-teller	And with that, his hand shook as he slowly took from the chest a small golden box and gently – ever so gently – opened the lid.
Lighthouse keeper	Ah, my little beauty. Still mine. Will you bring me death or joy? Only time will tell. Just another few years and you can pay me in my old age.
Story-teller	And with that, he stroked the box and gently put it back inside the chest as the great lamp flashed around him. Downstairs, as the storm raged on, his wife and daughter thought about lighting another candle.
Mother	I might light this night-light tonight.
Iris	Quite right as my eyesight's not bright in this moonlight.
Mother	It's the right night for night-lights.
Iris	Tonight's light is no bright light.
Mother	It's darker than midnight. I'm uptight with frost-bite.
Iris	Yes, it's the right night for night-lights tonight, too right!

Story-teller	So they did. But just as mother was about to put out the bottles for the milkman and take the stew off the stove, a heavy drumming came from the iron door.
Iris	Eek, what's that?
Mother	Didn't you hear? It's drumming coming from the great iron door.
Iris	On a night like this?
Mother	Then it can only mean one thing.
Iris	Oh, what? What is it, mother? What can it mean?
Mother	Someone wants to come in.
Story-teller	And with that, the great iron lighthouse door flew open and there against the roaring gale and lit only by a flash of lightning, stood . . .
Eye-patch Jake	Me!
Story-teller	Flash! Rumble! Roar! Swishshshshshshsh
Mother	Who?
Eye-patch Jake	I.
Iris	I?
Mother	I?

Eye-patch Jake	Oh no – only one eye . . . I've got one missing!
Story-teller	And with that, he fought with the great iron door . . . and won.
Eye-patch Jake	Take that! [*Punching and kicking*] And that! I am Eye-patch Jake and you're doomed.
Mother	Oh no, not Eye-patch Jake!
Iris	Not here in our kitchen?
Mother	Not Jake . . . with the eye-patch?
Iris	And slimy scar down his left cheek?
Mother	The pirate with blood on his hands and a price on his head?
Iris	Known as The Butcher of the Seas?
Eye-patch Jake	So you've heard of me?
Mother	No.
Story-teller	His greasy smile glistened in the candle-light. He oozed like an oil slick towards the two helpless women and whispered in a voice as thick as treacle.
Eye-patch Jake	I've come to seek my revenge.
Story-teller	With lips like melting lard, he

slobbered a kiss on the lighthouse keeper's daughter's pale cheek. His hand, like warm wax, seeped over her cold arm, his skin as greasy as dripping, as slippery as sludge and as smooth as a jellyfish.

Iris	Oh no!
Story-teller	Squelching like a slug towards her mother, Eye-patch Jake gave a slimy sneer and dribbled three words into her ear.
Eye-patch Jake	Where is he?
Mother	Who?
Eye-patch Jake	Him.
Mother	I can't think what you mean.
Eye-patch Jake	That man.
Mother	What man?
Eye-patch Jake	The man who lives here with you – the Lighthouse keeper.
Story-teller	His oily voice squelched like hair gel. His breath oozed like a swamp. His one eye moved like seeping frogspawn. His ugly scar twisted and shone like a slimy eel. He slithered like a blob of gunge across the

	floor ... Apart from that he seemed quite nice!
Eye-patch Jake	You don't like me much, do you?
Mother	Well ... er ... now you come to mention it ...
Story-teller	And with that, he grabbed them both and sat them down back to back as he pulled from inside his coat ... a rope.
Eye-patch Jake	Bah! This rope is made from the strongest fishing net. I've just used it for smoking kippers.
Iris	Why can't you smoke a pipe like most normal people?
Eye-patch Jake	I'll tie you both up. Then I'll find him. I know he's here somewhere. The rowing boat is tied up outside so he's still in. No one in their right mind would go out on a night like this.
Mother	Well you did.
Eye-patch Jake	Bah, shut up. He's upstairs, isn't he?
Story-teller	And with that, the vile man slid around them, pulling the rope tighter.
Eye-patch Jake	Round and round and round ...

Story-teller	Round and round and round . . .
Eye-patch Jake	Mmmm something in here smells good.
Story-teller	He hissed as he sniffed the steam from the pot on the stove. He oozed up to the Lighthouse keeper's wife and dribbled in a smarmy voice like hot toffee . . .
Eye-patch Jake	I've not had supper yet and I could do with a little bite.
Story-teller	So she bit him.
Eye-patch Jake	Bah, you'll pay for that. I only wanted a tot. Just a spot of hotpot.
Mother	Well untie this knot, I'll warm the pot and you can have the lot.
Eye-patch Jake	What rot! You forgot!
Mother	What?
Eye-patch Jake	I want the jackpot.
Iris	You crackpot.
Eye-patch Jake	Listen here, Miss Whatnot . . .
Mother	My husband's a good shot. He'll be back on the dot . . .
Eye-patch Jake	You fusspot. My plot is to blot out you lot.

13

Mother	You clot!
Eye-patch Jake	You what?
Iris	I hate you a lot, you're just a blood-shot tinpot slim-spot.
Eye-patch Jake	Bah! Stop all this grot! You've gone too far now. I've tied you up so tight that you'll never get out. So now to climb all the stairs and plunge my dagger into the Lighthouse keeper's back and rob him of a little something before I blow this place sky high.
Mother	You mean?
Eye-patch Jake	Yes, I've got enough gunpowder in my pockets to sink a ship. Ha ha ha.
Iris	Eeek!
Story-teller	And with those evil words still hanging in the air . . . [*Pause and silence*] And with those evil words still hanging in the air, he began to creep up those twisting lighthouse steps . . .
Eye-patch Jake	Round and up, round and up, round and up . . .
Story-teller	Up and round, up and round, up and round . . .

Eye-patch Jake	Higher and higher.
Story-teller	Faster and faster.
Eye-patch Jake	Round and up, round and up, round and up . . .
Story-teller	Much faster.
Eye-patch Jake	Yes, yes.
Story-teller	Faster . . . much faster . . .
Eye-patch Jake	I'm going as fast as I can. It's all right for you. You've got the easy bit.
Story-teller	Up and up and up.
Eye-patch Jake	Round and round and round.
Story-teller	Until at last he reached . . .
Eye-patch Jake	The top!
Story-teller	The Lighthouse keeper, a little worse for drink, had just closed the chest.
Lighthouse keeper	Who's there?
Eye-patch Jake	Me.
Lighthouse keeper	Eh?
Eye-patch Jake	One . . .
Lighthouse keeper	Where?
Eye-patch Jake	Eyed . . .

Lighthouse keeper	What?
Eye-patch Jake	Jake.
Lighthouse keeper	Who?
Eye-patch Jake	Jake.
Lighthouse keeper	Jake?
Eye-patch Jake	Yep.
Lighthouse keeper	One-eyed Jake?
Eye-patch Jake	Got it! Yes, I'm the pirate with one eye called Jake.
Lighthouse keeper	Oh really? So what's your other eye called?
Eye-patch Jake	And I spy with my little eye something called ... revenge! I've dreamed of this time and now it's here. I've found you at last and revenge will be sweet.
Lighthouse keeper	You'll never make me talk. You'll never get away with it. My lips are shut.
Eye-patch Jake	I've got a sharp knife here.
Lighthouse keeper	What do you want to know?
Story-teller	The flashing light from the lamp caught the glinting blade of Jake's

knife. The Lighthouse keeper lost his cool.

Eye-patch Jake	Get up. What are you doing down there on your hands and knees?
Lighthouse keeper	It's my cool – I've lost it. It must be here somewhere!
Eye-patch Jake	You know what I want.
Lighthouse keeper	Yes, I know.
Eye-patch Jake	And I know too.
Lighthouse keeper	Oh I know you know.
Eye-patch Jake	And I know you know I know.
Lighthouse keeper	I know.
Story-teller	He knew.
Eye-patch Jake	I know too.
Story-teller	He knew too.
Eye-patch Jake	And you're now a dead man. I've been keeping an eye out for you for a long time.
Lighthouse keeper	So that's why it's missing.
Story-teller	The Lighthouse keeper was playing for time as the ice-cold steel blade flashed silver in the blackness. It was then that it came to him in a flash.

Lighthouse keeper	Aha!
Eye-patch Jake	What?
Lighthouse keeper	A flash!
Story-teller	And with that, he swung round the great light to flash and flare right into Jake's one eye.
Eye-patch Jake	Aaaaargh!
Story-teller	The Lighthouse keeper kicked the knife from his slippery hand . . . and the long struggle began . . .
Lighthouse keeper	Two eyes are better than one. [*They wrestle*]
Eye-patch Jake	A dirty trick.
Story-teller	But as the two men pulled and tugged, punched and kicked, pushed and gripped, they began to tumble . . . down the lighthouse steps.
Lighthouse keeper	Aaah . . . eek ouch umph!
Eye-patch Jake	I'll kill you for this. Ouch!
Story-teller	Round and round and round, down and down and down . . . swirling down and round, bumping every step . . . until the Lighthouse keeper cracked his head and slumped in a heap.

Eye-patch Jake	Ha ha! Knocked out! It won't be long now before I get what I want. First I shall search his pockets ...
Story-teller	Meanwhile, down in the kitchen, the rope was working loose.
Mother	It's a good thing that rope smells of kippers.
Story-teller	The cat had been good enough to chew through the last few threads ...
Iris	We're free! Quick, we must go to father's rescue.
Story-teller	And with that, they sprang to their feet, grabbed a candle and a rolling-pin and began the long climb upwards ... just as Eye-patch Jake began dragging the Lighthouse keeper to the top.
Eye-patch Jake	Up and up, round and round ...
Story-teller	Round and round and up and up ...
Mother	Up and round up and round ...
Iris	Round and up and round and up ...
Eye-patch Jake	Higher, ever higher...
Story-teller	Step after step after step ...
Mother	One after another after another ...

Iris	Upwards ever upwards . . .
Eye-patch Jake	Round and round.
Story-teller	Up and up.
Mother	Up and round.
Iris	Round and up.
Story-teller	Until at last . . .
Eye-patch Jake	We've reached the top!
Story-teller	Fumbling in the flashing darkness, Eye-patch Jake caught sight of his dagger glinting on the floor . . . while the two women climbed on and on . . .
Mother	Round and round.
Iris	Up and up.
Eye-patch Jake	Ah ha ha, just enough time to cut his throat . . .
Mother	Until at last . . .
Iris	We've reached the top!
Story-teller	But before Eye-patch Jake could make a stab and sink the icy steel into his victim, the Lighthouse keeper's wife coshed him with her rolling-pin and he slithered to the floor in a trickle of slime.

Mother	Take that, you worm.
Iris	It's gone so quiet.
Story-teller	There was deathly silence. The air was so tense it could be cut with a knife so it was lucky the dagger was out of reach.
Mother	It's as quiet as a pin.
Iris	You can even hear a mouse dropping. Look, father is knocked out!
Mother	Then help me with Eye-patch Jake.
Eye-patch Jake	Ergh – where am I?
Lighthouse keeper	Ergh – who hit me?
Iris	What can we do? He's coming round.
Story-teller	An idea suddenly hit her.
Mother	Ouch.
Iris	What was that?
Mother	It was an idea. It suddenly hit me. We'll lock him up in that chest, the key is still in it. Then we'll drag it up onto the roof up those steps. He'll be out of the way till we get the police.
Iris	Won't he freeze to death out there on a night like this?

Mother	It serves him right if he does – but we can throw a candle in with him for warmth.
Story-teller	And with that, they put him in the chest, after taking out the little golden box.
Mother	I can't think what this is. More junk to throw away in the morning.
Story-teller	And with that they slowly – very slowly – climbed the last few steps. They dragged the chest behind them up onto the roof . . .
Iris	Push. Up and round . . .
Mother	Pull. Round and up . . .
Story-teller	Panting and puffing, bit by bit, step by step, they came to the hatch which led out onto the small roof hundreds of metres above the angry rocks below. The icy wind tore at the hatch as it opened. One gust of the icy blast and they could be swept away for ever . . .
Mother	Hold on tight . . .
Iris	Hark at that wind . . .
Story-teller	Wooooshshshshsh swishshshshsh roarrrrrrr rumble brbrrrrrrrr.

Iris	Help, I'm slipping.
Mother	Quick, get back below.
Story-teller	Just as a gust ripped through the night sky, they shut the hatch and left the chest out in the storm.
Mother	Down we go . . .
Iris	Down and round and down . . .
Mother	We'll have to get your father down to the kitchen.
Iris	But that means we'll have to carry him!
Story-teller	And with that, they held his feet and his arms and began the downward trudge . . .
Iris	Down and down and down . . .
Mother	Round and round and round . . .
Story-teller	Step by step by step.
Iris	Phew! He's heavy.
Story-teller	Gulping, gasping, panting, puffing . . .
Iris	Down and down . . .
Mother	Round and down.
Lighthouse keeper	Groan and ouch.

Story-teller	In a downward spiral.
Iris	Down and down and down.
Lighthouse keeper	Put me down a minute. [*They do and he takes a nip from his flask*] Eeh, that's better.
Mother	Round and round and round.
Story-teller	Down and round.
Lighthouse keeper	Round and down.
Mother	Until at last . . .
Iris	We've reached the ground.
Story-teller	And with that they put the Lighthouse keeper in a chair by the fire, while they took a quick rest. [*They sit*] But they had no time to lose. [*They stand*]
Mother	My dear, there's only one thing for it. Your father's too ill, I'm too old and there's an evil man up there in a chest on the roof. He could break out at any time and murder the lot of us. Look, here's a bag of money – our life-savings. No one is going to take that from us now. Iris, you've got to take it to somewhere safe.
Iris	But mother, what can I do? I'll never be able to spend it tonight.

Mother	No, no, my child. You've got to get away quickly and take this with you. Quick, the boat is tied up outside.
Iris	But mother, the sea is so wild tonight. The waves are so high. The wind is so strong. The air is so cold. The storm is so fierce. The night is so dark. The boat is so small. The rocks are so sharp. The land is so far. The gale is so rough. I am so tired. The sea is so deep.
Mother	But don't let a little thing like that put you off.
Iris	But just hark at that storm, mother. The night is in a rage.
Mother	Well, yes I agree it's a little damp so make sure you take an umbrella. Iris, you've got to do this – for all of us. Save us all.
Iris	Mother – I will do my best.
Story-teller	And as they walked to the door, her mother gave her their life-savings and they both shed a tear. It was such a sad moment that even the cat wept into its milk. The great door was opened and the roar of the storm

filled the room. Wooooshshshshsh Roarrrrrrr shshshshshshsh.

Mother	Just do what you can, Iris, my child.
Story-teller	WOOOOSHSHSHSHSH CRASHSHSHSHSHSH RUMBLE SPLASHHSHSHSHSHSH . . .
Iris	What did you say, mother?
Mother	Row to land. Go straight to the police station. It's gone midnight but you'll have to wake him up.
Story-teller	WOOOSH CRASH RUMBLE ROAR HOWWWWWL SWISHSHSHSH . . .
Iris	What? I can't hear a word.
Mother	Get PC Kripps and bring him here.
Story-teller	GROWWWWL CRACK! SMASHSHSHSH CRRUNCHCHCHCHCH!
Mother	GET PC KRIPPS AND BRING HIM HERE.
Story-teller	WHINE. . . BOOOOOM! BLAST . . .
Iris	Are you sure?
Mother	What? Eh?
Iris	Then farewell, mother. I will do my best.

Story-teller	While the storm raged on, the poor girl sat in the boat with barnacles on the bottom (the boat, not the girl!). Mother shut the great iron door and went back to her poor husband. It was just as well she shut the door for the very next moment a wave knocked the purse of money from the girl's hand and sent it spinning out into the sea. She screamed and sobbed but the roar of the storm drowned her feeble cries. And with that the boat spun on the waves and she was taken away into the cruel night. There was a flash in the sky. It was like a rocket shooting up from the top of the lighthouse . . .
Mother	Dear, can you hear me? Oh you're so cold. Just hark at that thunder up there at the roof.
Lighthouse keeper	Why yes, it sounds more like cannon-fire than thunder.
Mother	Like a bomb or . . .
Story-teller	It was then that she remembered Eye-patch Jake up in the chest, with the gunpowder – and the candle.
Mother	Oh dear! I must just pop upstairs. You wait here and eat your stew.

Story-teller	And so began her climb up to the roof – alone in the dark and cold.
Mother	Up and up and round and round . . .
Story-teller	Higher and higher.
Mother	Up and round.
Story-teller	Upward, ever upward . . .
Mother	Round and up.
Story-teller	Quicker and quicker.
Mother	Higher and higher.
Story-teller	Faster and faster.
Mother	Step by step.
Story-teller	Faster, much faster.
Mother	If I went any faster I'd drill my head into the roof.
Story-teller	Puffing . . .
Mother	Panting . . .
Story-teller	Twirling . . .
Mother	Swirling . . .
Story-teller	Hurling . . .
Mother	Curling . . .
Story-teller	Getting much higher.

Mother	Getting worn out!
Story-teller	Past the great flashing lamp . . .
Mother	And up the last few steps . . .
Story-teller	Fit to drop, she had the feeling . . .
Mother	What relief, I've reached the ceiling!
Story-teller	And with that, she pushed open the hatch and peeped out into the churning night.
Mother	Oh lummy! It's gone!
Story-teller	All that was left on a scorched patch of the roof was a trickle of green slime. The whole chest with Eye-patch Jake inside had been blown sky-high. Blown to . . .
Mother	Smithereens! Gone. Blown to . . .
Story-teller	Kingdom come!
Mother	Well it serves him right if you ask me. A shame about the chest, though. I'll have to go down and break the news. My husband was very fond of that chest and the junk inside . . .
Story-teller	And with that, she began the plod back down.
Mother	Here we go again . . .

Story-teller	Downward, ever downward.
Mother	Bit by bit.
Story-teller	Step by step.
Mother	Down and round.
Story-teller	Round and down.
Mother	Twisting and turning.
Story-teller	Swirling like a whirlpool.
Mother	Twirling like a corkscrew.
Story-teller	Round and down.
Mother	Down and round.
Story-teller	Until at last . . .
Mother	I've reached the ground!
Lighthouse keeper	What kept you? I've run out of rum. Go down in the cellar for me, would you? It's only another three flights of steps.
Mother	You must be joking! You'll be pleased to hear he's gone.
Lighthouse keeper	Who?
Mother	Him.
Lighthouse keeper	Gone?

Mother	Gone!
Lighthouse keeper	When?
Mother	Now.
Lighthouse keeper	Where?
Mother	Up.
Lighthouse keeper	Up?
Mother	Out.
Lighthouse keeper	How?
Mother	Bang!
Lighthouse keeper	Bang?
Mother	Zoom!
Lighthouse keeper	Where?
Mother	Roof.
Lighthouse keeper	Why?
Mother	Chest.
Lighthouse keeper	Chest?
Mother	Fire.
Lighthouse keeper	Fire?
Mother	Flash.
Lighthouse keeper	Flash?

Mother	Blown up.
Lighthouse keeper	Gone?
Mother	Yes.
Lighthouse keeper	Blimey!
Story-teller	And with that he lept from his seat with sweat dripping from his brow.
Lighthouse keeper	My chest has gone? Crikey!
Mother	Yes. Blown up – with him in it.
Lighthouse keeper	Nothing left?
Mother	Only a trickle of green slime.
Lighthouse keeper	But . . . but oh no, this can't be. What about . . .
Story-teller	And with that, he staggered to the steps. Feeble as he was, he began to climb those twisting stairs . . .
Lighthouse keeper	Up and round and up and round.
Story-teller	Up and up and up.
Lighthouse keeper	Round and round and round.
Story-teller	Whipping in a whirlwind.
Lighthouse keeper	Wafting in a typhoon.
Story-teller	Climbing ever higher.
Lighthouse keeper	Upward ever upward.

Story-teller	Step by step by step.
Lighthouse keeper	Stair after stair after stair.
Story-teller	Up and round.
Lighthouse keeper	Round and up. I feel proper poorly.
Story-teller	Until at last . . .
Lighthouse keeper	I've reached the top! Phew!
Story-teller	In the darkness, lit every few seconds by the blinding flash, the poor, tired and sad lighthouse keeper gave a weak sigh.
Lighthouse keeper	Haaa.
Story-teller	And with that, something golden caught his eye.
Lighthouse keeper	Ouch.
Story-teller	The box – it was there on the ground.
Lighthouse keeper	It is here, my little beauty. But the question is . . . is it empty?
Story-teller	With shaking fingers, he stooped down, picked it up and slowly lifted the lid.
Lighthouse keeper	Ha ha! It's here! I've still got it.
Story-teller	And looking up at him from the box, on a cushion of black velvet, stared . . . an eye.

Lighthouse keeper	Eye-patch Jake won't be wanting you again, my beauty. So now you're mine, all mine – forever. No one can take you away from me now.
Story-teller	As the lamp flashed around him, the eye in the box seemed to wink. It was red and shone like a jewel. So with a song in his heart and a sparkle in his eyes (all three of them), he once again began the downward climb . . .
Lighthouse keeper	Down and down and down.
Story-teller	Round and round and round.
Lighthouse keeper	Whipping round like a whisk.
Story-teller	Skipping down in a helter-skelter.
Lighthouse keeper	Spinning in a spiral.
Story-teller	Curling in a coil.
Lighthouse keeper	Turning in a tornado.
Story-teller	Sinking in a swirl.
Lighthouse keeper	Downward, ever downward.
Story-teller	Gurgling down the plughole.
Lighthouse keeper	Veering in a vortex.
Story-teller	Round and down.
Lighthouse keeper	Down and round.

Story-teller	Until at last . . .
Lighthouse keeper	I've reached the ground!
Mother	Oh there you are. Why are you grinning from ear to ear?
Lighthouse keeper	I've found it. I've got it. It's here. Now it's mine!
Story-teller	And with that, he opened the box.
Mother	Eeeeek! It's an eye, a horrible bloodshot eye. Take it away. What on earth do you want that thing for?
Lighthouse keeper	It's a long story. You'd better sit down, my dear.
Story-teller	She sat down and waited to hear her husband's secret.
Lighthouse keeper	Many years ago . . . long before we met, I was . . . I was . . . a pirate.
Mother	Gosh.
Lighthouse keeper	I got into some bad ways I'm afraid to say – and I got into a bad crowd. Would you believe I worked for Eye-patch Jake? Well I did . . . but he had two eyes then because he wore a false one . . . this one here.
Mother	Gosh.

Lighthouse keeper	Well one day I saw the light. It wasn't for me. I'd had enough of being a thug so I told him I was off.
Mother	Gosh.
Lighthouse keeper	He flew into a rage and we had a fight with knives. I just got away without my throat being cut but in all the fighting – his false eye popped out.
Mother	Oh my gosh.
Lighthouse keeper	It wasn't till I took off my shirt that night that I found it – it had gone down my vest! It was stuck in my belly-button and staring up at me. I knew then that it wasn't just a glass eye but something of real value.
Mother	Gosh.
Lighthouse keeper	It was a huge ruby, worth a fortune. The safest place for him to keep it where he could keep a close eye on it, was in his face! But now I had it!
Mother	Well I never!
Lighthouse keeper	So I knew he would never rest till he tracked me down and got it back. It took him all these years to find me. But now he's gone, we can keep this. Yes, this eye will see us into our old

	age! We're rich. We'll never have to worry about money again.
Mother	Super! Let's go straight away.
Lighthouse keeper	No. I once made a promise. When I left Jake's pirate ship, I told myself I would pay back all the wrong I had done. Instead of robbing ships, I would help to save them. Instead of drowning sailors, I would save them from the rocks. So that is what I have done. For twenty years I have lit that lamp up there. I have never let it go out at night – not even tonight.
Story-teller	And with that, or rather with a hanky, his wife wiped a tear from her cheek. Even the cat was moved as it dabbed a paw over its dripping eyelash.
Lighthouse keeper	So you see, I always knew we were in danger of his revenge. But from now on we can all sleep safely in our beds. We should be glad so why are you crying?
Mother	It's our daughter. I shall never rest until Iris returns. Oh what have I done? Fancy sending her out on a night like this.
Lighthouse keeper	But my dear, it's almost morning and

	haven't you noticed?
Story-teller	Woosh, zoom, clunk, plop!
Lighthouse keeper	The wind has dropped. The waves are calm and the sun will soon rise. Just listen . . .
Story-teller	As a golden sun began to appear above the sea, the small rowing boat drifted up to the rocks. Inside, Iris pulled at the oars, stepped out and made her way up to the great iron door.
Mother	Yes . . . listen . . . it's, it's our daughter! She's come back!
Story-teller	And with that, they opened that great iron door and the three of them hugged.
Iris	Mother!
Mother	Darling!
Iris	Father!
Lighthouse keeper	Darling!
Mother	Darling!
Lighthouse keeper	Darling!
Story-teller	The cat just smiled.
Mother	But Iris, where is PC Kripps?

38

Iris	Who?
Mother	PC Kripps from the police station. I sent you to fetch him.
Iris	Did you? I thought you wanted these.
Story-teller	She held out a paper bag. Her mother took it and looked inside.
Mother	But dear, I asked you to get PC Kripps and bring him here!
Iris	Oh dear! I thought you said GET CHEESY CRISPS AND BRING SOME BEER! I've been to the pub. I had to wake them up. Please don't be cross.
Mother	Of course not, dear. It was very windy, after all. Just as well you had my money!
Story-teller	And with that, the poor girl broke down in helpless sobs.
Lighthouse keeper	Oh please don't cry. You'll soak the cat.
Mother	Whatever is the matter, my child?
Iris	Your life-savings, mother . . . they're at the bottom of the sea. They've gone. I'll never be able to live with myself.
Mother	Oh, think nothing of it.

Lighthouse keeper	We won't need them now!
Iris	What? What do you mean?
Mother	It's a long story. Come and sit down by the fire and we'll tell you all about it over a nice pot of tea.
Story-teller	And with that, the three of them sat down and once again the Lighthouse keeper began the long tale . . .
Lighthouse keeper	Well, it was like this, my girl . . . it all started a long time ago. It was a dark and stormy night . . .
Story-teller	Crash!
Mother	Eeek, what's that?
Story-teller	It was day-break. And with that, a burst of golden sunshine poured into the room. Out across the waves to the east, the light shone crimson over the rolling sea, where it met the morning sky in a blaze of orange . . . and a ray of hope!
Iris	Wonderful!
Mother	Magic!
Lighthouse keeper	So there you have it!

Story-teller

Our tale is told. It must be said,
One-eyed Jake is clearly dead.
It must be said our tale is told,
The Lighthouse keeper had his gold.
That ruby eye fetched quite a price,
A fortune that was rather nice!
They moved away and joy was theirs . . .
No more they trod those blooming stairs!
Their ups and downs had gone, and so
They bought a cosy bungalow!
No more would waves crash out and in,
Even the cat was seen to grin.
Its tea was cream, its bed, a box . . .
No more was milk served on the rocks!